BEYOND TRAUMA

A Healing Journey for Women

PARTICIPANT'S WORKBOOK

Stephanie S. Covington

with Kary Young

■ HAZELDEN®

Hazelden
Center City, Minnesota 55012-0176

1-800-328-9000
1-651-213-4590 (Fax)
www.hazelden.org

To request permission, write to Permissions Coordinator,
Hazelden, P.O. Box 176, Center City, MN 55012-0176.
To purchase additional copies of this publication,
call 1-800-328-9000 or 1-651-213-4000.

ISBN: 1-59285-069-3

Cover design by David Spohn
Interior design and typesetting by Kinne Design

Hazelden Publishing and Educational Services is a division of the Hazelden Foundation, a
not-for-profit organization. Since 1949, Hazelden has been a leader in promoting the dignity and treatment of people afflicted with the disease of chemical dependency.

The mission of the foundation is to improve the quality of life for individuals, families, and
communities by providing a national continuum of information, education, and recovery services that
are widely accessible; to advance the field through research and training; and to improve our quality
and effectiveness through continuous improvement and innovation.

Stemming from that, the mission of this division is to provide quality information and support
to people wherever they may be in their personal journey—from education and early intervention,
through treatment and recovery, to personal and spiritual growth.

Although our treatment programs do not necessarily use everything Hazelden publishes, our
bibliotherapeutic materials support our mission and the Twelve Step philosophy upon which it is
based. We encourage your comments and feedback.

The headquarters of the Hazelden Foundation are in Center City, Minnesota. Additional treatment facilities are located in Chicago, Illinois; Newberg, Oregon; New York, New York; Plymouth,
Minnesota; St. Paul, Minnesota; and West Palm Beach, Florida. At these sites, we provide a continuum
of care for men and women of all ages. Our Plymouth facility is designed specifically for youth
and families.

For more information on Hazelden,
please call **1-800-257-7800.**

Or you may access our World Wide Web site
on the Internet at **www.hazelden.org.**

CONTENTS

INTRODUCTION

Starting anything new usually produces mixed feelings—often both anxiety (or fear) and excitement. As you begin the *Beyond Trauma: A Healing Journey for Women* program, this may be your first experience looking at trauma in your life. Or this may be a journey that you have started and stopped at different periods in your life. Either way, we know that awareness and knowledge are the first steps toward change and growth.

In the *Beyond Trauma* program, women's ways of "knowing" are valued and central to developing a deeper understanding of trauma. Your group will give you a place to explore and try new things in a safe, nurturing, and supportive environment.

There are exercises that you will do as a group and others in the workbook that you can do on your own (or with another group member). You may also want to take notes as you discuss topics in the group. Feel free to write down questions that arise, observations, or new thoughts and feelings that emerge.

In your group, you will go through a process of

- learning more about what trauma is and how widespread it is in women's lives

- exploring how trauma and abuse have impacted you

- developing coping mechanisms, doing exercises to help you feel grounded, and focusing on safety

You have space in this workbook to explore your life experiences and the world around you. This is your own personal journal where you can write down your feelings, thoughts, and ideas and have an opportunity to try out new ways of coping with the impact of trauma on your life.

Duplicating this page is illegal. Do not copy this material without written permission from the publisher.

1

In using this kind of workbook, you will see the strengths you have and increase the skills that move you further along in your life journey. Remember, you are not alone. The connections you make with women in this group, combined with your courage to explore the trauma you have experienced, can bring you a greater sense of empowerment and energy to continue the path toward healing. Many women before you have walked the road to recovery and healing and they will be with you in spirit.

Wishing you the best,

Stephanie S. Covington

Stephanie S. Covington

The Connections between Violence, Abuse, and Trauma

Personal growth, recovery, and healing are a lifelong journey. If we take the risk of learning about trauma and give ourselves the opportunity to explore the process of healing, we can grow and cope and live happy and healthy lives.

Trauma

- Impacts inner self: It can impact our inner lives—our thoughts, feelings, beliefs, values. For example, some women believe that "you can't trust anyone," and "the world is a very unsafe place."

- Impacts outer self: It can impact our outer lives—our outer life is our relationships and behavior. Many women who have experienced trauma struggle with their relationships—families, friends, sexual relationships. For example, parenting is a relationship that can become even more complicated by the experience of trauma. Some women who have experienced childhood abuse may be triggered back to their abuse experience by their own child. The risk of this happening is greatest when a women's child becomes the age she was when the abuse first occurred.

   Another part of our outer self is our behavior. Some women become numb, isolated, and asexual. For other women, their behavior is at the opposite end of the continuum. They may become agitated, loud, and often hypersexual.

A major part of the healing process is becoming congruent. This means having your inner self (thoughts, feelings, beliefs) connected to, and consistent with, your outer self (behavior and relationships). For example, does your face (outer self) reflect how you are feeling (inner self)?

Duplicating this page is illegal. Do not copy this material without written permission from the publisher.

3

If you have experienced trauma, you may struggle with questions like these:

- Why did this happen to me?

- What did I do wrong?

- Why do I feel so ashamed?

- Why did people hurt me?

- Why is life such a struggle?

- What do I do now?

This group provides a safe space to explore your thoughts and feelings. You may find that many of the questions you have are similar to those of other women in the group. It's important that you realize there is hope. Many women are recovering from their traumatic experiences. The healing journey can be challenging, but it can be filled with support from the women in this group and others in your life.

What Is Trauma?

Trauma is any stressor that occurs in a sudden and forceful way and is experienced as overwhelming. Women who have experienced traumatic events describe feelings of intense fear, helplessness, or horror. These are normal reactions to abnormal or extreme situations.

We know that no two people experience trauma in the same way. Many things influence how a woman responds to a traumatic event: her age, history with other trauma, family dynamics, support systems, and more. We know that what may be a traumatic event for one person may not be for another. Sometimes, trauma has occurred but may not be recognized immediately because the person may see violent or abusive events as normal.

Understanding trauma and that we each respond to it differently will help us be supportive and nonjudgmental toward each other. Women need support to heal from trauma. Part of the process in healing from trauma, like recovering from addiction, is developing connection and support with others.

Trauma Takes Many Forms

Trauma can take many forms: emotional, sexual, or physical abuse; painful or frightening medical procedures; catastrophic injuries and illnesses; rape or assault; domestic violence; muggings; burglary; witnessing murder; automobile accidents; abandonment (especially for small children); culturally bound, intergenerational trauma (e.g., Native Americans); immigration; natural disasters (hurricanes, earthquakes, tornadoes, fires, floods, volcanoes); terrorism (such as September 11, 2001); witnessing violence (such as a parent harming another parent); loss of a loved one and severe bereavements (including a pet); combat/war; torture; kidnapping; etc. Of all these forms of trauma that women and men can experience, women are at a much greater risk of interpersonal violence than men.

Post-Traumatic Stress Disorder

The effects of traumatic victimization often result in something called post-traumatic stress disorder (PTSD). PTSD symptoms are generally grouped into three categories. You may recognize some of these symptoms from your own experience. It often feels comforting to know that there is a name for what you are experiencing, to know that you are not alone, and to know there are people who understand and can help. Here are the three categories of PTSD symptoms:

1. Reexperiencing (includes disturbed sleep, intrusive memories, distressing dreams, nightmares, flashbacks, reliving the event, a view of the world as unsafe).

2. Numbing and avoidance (mistrust of others, isolation and disconnection, emotional or "psychic" numbness, low self-esteem, neglect of health, dissociation, ability to remember memories or feelings but not both, memory loss for certain events, loss of faith and hope).

3. Hyperarousal (intense emotions, difficulty sleeping, panic and anxiousness, self-harm, risky behaviors, irritability, anger, difficulty concentrating) (American Psychiatric Association 2000).

In your group sessions, you will explore together your responses to different situations. This will help you understand why you respond the way you do in certain situations, and together you will learn and teach each other new ways of responding.

How Often Trauma Occurs

It can be helpful to look at statistics to give us an idea of how often traumatic events occur in the lives of women and girls. This can help us feel less isolated, alone, or at fault for the abuse.

- One out of every four girls will be sexually abused before the age of fourteen (Hopper 1998).

- The National Crime Victimization Survey found that, in 1996, more than two-thirds of the rapes and sexual assaults committed in the United States remained unreported (Ringel 1997).

- There are four million cases of domestic violence in the United States each year. A woman is beaten every fifteen seconds (Bureau of Justice Statistics 1998).

- The negative effects on a child who witnesses violence against his or her mother (secondary victimization) appear to be low self-esteem, behavioral problems, reduced social competence, depression, and anxiety (Carlson 1990).

- Women offenders have been victims of abuse six to ten times more often than women in the general population (Pollock 2002).

- Women can be traumatized (or retraumatized if they have already experienced trauma in their lives) by the standard operating practices in criminal justice settings (denial of privacy, body searches, restraints, isolation) (Bloom, Owen, and Covington 2003).

"I felt I was the only one who had experienced so much abuse.

And what I came to realize is that I am not alone."

Substance Abuse and Trauma

You can see how frequently abuse occurs in women's lives. For many women, trauma and substance abuse are linked. Women who abuse substances have higher rates of childhood physical and sexual abuse than men and non-substance-abusing women. Some women use alcohol and other drugs, or addictive behaviors such as overeating, overworking, and gambling, to help ease the pain of abuse (Covington and Surrey 1997). In addition, women who abuse alcohol and other drugs are more vulnerable to being abused.

EXERCISE

CREATING SAFETY

In the group, you imagined a comfortable, secure place: your chair, your bed, a place in your imagination or past, the beach, a meadow. In the space below, draw a picture of what you visualized in the group.

Duplicating this page is illegal. Do not copy this material without written permission from the publisher.

7

H O M E W O R K

The picture or symbol that you've drawn can be used to calm and comfort yourself.
Continue to focus on various ways to soothe yourself.

1. Name some ways you have taken care of yourself when you have been afraid.

   _____

   _____

   _____

   _____

2. What are some other things you can imagine doing in the future?

   _____

   _____

   _____

   _____

3. Write about an experience where you calmed yourself, or write about the ways you
   have seen or heard other women take care of themselves.

   _____

   _____

   _____

   _____

4. Work on drawing your symbol or souvenir. You might want to make copies of it to
   keep in your pocket or purse, hang on a mirror, or keep in a locker.

For the next session, try to find an object that will remind you of your symbol or souvenir
and bring it to the next group meeting. (This may not be possible if you are in a criminal
justice setting).

REFLECTION

This is the place in your journal where you write or draw about your experience in the group. Maybe you'd like to write about what was most meaningful for you in the first session.

_____

_____

_____

_____

_____

_____

_____

_____

_____

_____

_____

Power and Abuse

In the first session, we began to look at abuse, violence, and trauma in women's lives. We recognized we are not alone in our journey. The next step is to see the connection between power and abuse. In your group, you did the role-reversal exercise. Messages received by women in our society were switched and given to men and vice versa.

When the roles were reversed, who was at risk to be abused?

In the fantasy, who had the most power?

In reality (the opposite of fantasy), men have more power in our society, and women are at greater risk for abuse. Sometimes it is easier to see the connection between power and abuse in the role-reversal exercise than it is to see it in the world we live in.

Here are some ways that power and abuse are connected:

- Abuser uses power over victim.

- Abuse takes power away from the victim.

- Victim feels powerless against abuser and in many aspects of her life.

- Victim feels trapped or locked in a role.

- Victim feels isolated, so there is no strength or power from others who could help.

GROUNDING

You may find yourself feeling uncomfortable and distracted at times or having negative feelings. Grounding techniques are ways to detach or disconnect from inner emotional discomfort by focusing on the outer world. Grounding is one way to become empowered.

> With your eyes open, remind yourself of your name, your age, where you are now, the day of the week, the date, and the city. Then notice the environment you are in—the size of the room, color of the walls, furniture in the room, pictures on the wall, height of the ceiling, and so on.

This is an exercise you can use in or out of group. It may be helpful when doing some of the homework exercises.

HOMEWORK

THE POWER AND CONTROL WHEEL

The Power and Control Wheel is divided into parts or segments. Each of these represents ways someone can be abusive to another.

(Duluth Domestic Abuse Intervention Project, 202 East Superior Street, Duluth, MN 55802.)

Give examples of these types of abuse:

- physical abuse _____

- sexual abuse _____

- emotional abuse _____

- economic abuse _____

- coercion and threats _____

- intimidation _____

- isolation _____

- minimizing, denying, blaming _____

- using children _____

- using male privilege _____

REFLECTION

What is one thing you want to remember from this session?

_____

_____

_____

_____

_____

_____

_____

Reactions to Trauma

There are many kinds of traumatic events, and there are many different responses to trauma. One form of trauma is interpersonal violence, or abuse. There are different kinds of abuse; emotional, physical, and sexual abuse are some common types. Women, more than men, are at risk for this kind of trauma. Responses to trauma in women's lives can also be very different. There are emotional responses, which happen internally, in the inner self. There are responses that are external and show up in behavior, or the outer self. And there are physical reactions that show up in the body.

Types of Abuse

- *Emotional abuse* includes playing mind games, name-calling, constant criticizing, withholding approval or affection as punishment, humiliating someone publicly or privately, abusing pets, threatening, manipulating, and blaming.

- *Physical abuse* includes pushing, slapping, kicking, choking, locking someone out of the house, threatening someone with a weapon, harassing someone to the point of physical illness, restraining (holding someone down, pinning the person's arms), depriving someone of sleep, biting, shaking, spitting, and deliberately giving someone a sexually transmitted disease.

- *Sexual abuse* includes rape, coercion, unwanted or inappropriate touch, sex after a beating or an illness, sexual criticism, forcing sex in front of others, treating others as sex objects, and nonconsensual sadistic sexual acts.

Symptoms Associated with Trauma

Here are some of the reactions that women often have if they have experienced a traumatic event (e.g., interpersonal violence, auto accident, natural disaster).

Remember, traumatic events can overwhelm a woman physically and psychologically.

Physical reactions

Sometimes women have difficulty breathing (panting, rapid breathing), their heart pounds, their thoughts race, their muscles are tense, and they have cold sweats. They may also experience a great deal of tension in their bodies.

Feelings of helplessness, immobility, or freezing may also occur. It's been said that if hyperarousal is the accelerator of the nervous system, immobility is its brake. When both occur at the same time, a feeling of overwhelming helplessness and powerlessness results. This is not a perception. The body feels truly paralyzed.

Psychological reactions

Some women disconnect from what is happening at the moment. There is a body-mind split. This is one of the most common psychological reactions, and it is called *dissociation*—the mind just seems to leave the body. Women experience this as "losing time." Psychic numbing can also occur. It's also not uncommon for abused women to use denial in their lives because the truth about their abuse is too painful.

Some symptoms show up immediately following a traumatic event. Some show up later. When this happens, the feelings a woman experiences are often very real and vivid, as if the event were actually happening all over again. It is important to listen to your body and understand how one or more, or a cluster, of these symptoms may be a reason to seek additional help and to learn about the impact that trauma has had on your life.

Here are some symptoms that may be experienced immediately:

- sleep disturbance, nightmares
- exaggerated emotional and startled reactions to noises, quick movements, etc.
- hyperactivity, restlessness
- hypervigilance
- abrupt mood swings

- fear of going crazy
- flashbacks
- sensitivity to sound, light, smell, taste, touch
- fear of losing control
- a desire for alcohol or other drugs

Here are some symptoms that may develop later:

- panic attacks, anxiety, phobias
- mental blankness or being "spacey"
- avoidance behavior
- attraction to dangerous situations
- frequent anger or crying
- exaggerated or diminished sexual activity
- amnesia and forgetfulness
- inability to love, nurture, or bond with other individuals
- fear of dying or having a shortened life
- self-harming behavior
- cravings (particularly if chemically dependent)

And here's a list of symptoms that may take even longer to develop:

- fatigue or low energy
- physical health problems, such as a depleted immune system, thyroid dysfunction, psychosomatic illnesses such as neck and back problems, asthma, digestive distress, spastic colon, severe premenstrual syndrome
- eating disorders
- diminished emotional responses
- inability to make commitments
- depression
- feelings of isolation, detachment
- reduced ability to make decisions, formulate plans, and carry them out

▶ As you go through these lists, which symptoms have you experienced?

_____	_____
_____	_____
_____	_____
_____	_____
_____	_____

Trauma and the Brain

Trauma also impacts how the brain functions. People under extreme stress often process and organize information differently. For example, research on the brain has shown that child abuse, one form of trauma, can cause serious damage to the structure and functioning of the developing brain itself. Extreme stress can change the brain to cause a person to exhibit various antisocial, though adaptive, behaviors. Physical, emotional, or sexual abuse or any other major stress can set off a series of physical changes that alter a child's brain in order for it to cope with a dangerous world.

When trauma impacts the brain, it can result in emotional changes. Problems such as dissociation, flashbacks, and confusion (racing or jumbled thoughts), which we discussed earlier, may all stem from the impact of trauma on the brain. Fear from a traumatic event is experienced in the mind. Some people experience and reexperience these thoughts even though they do not want to have them and try not to have them.

Many women talk about frightening thoughts "invading" their minds— sometimes at uncontrollable times (after something triggers their memory of the traumatic event) and in their dreams. Nightmares are not uncommon. Sometimes a woman may have "night terrors," where she wakes up screaming and sweating yet cannot recall what she was dreaming about. This can make the woman feel that, even when she is in her bed, at home, during the night, she still is not safe. Sometimes these invasions in her mind make her feel like she is going crazy or losing control of her mind.

▶ Have you ever experienced this kind of thing? Please explain.

_____

_____

_____

_____

Trauma can also cause problems like depression, anxiety, rage, and feelings of chronic emptiness. There is also a connection with addiction. Understanding that trauma can change brain chemistry (just like substance abuse can change brain chemistry) can help you see the connection between trauma and what is going on physically and emotionally. With changes in brain chemistry, women are at a greater risk for substance abuse, eating disorders, self-harming behavior, and mental health problems.

�֎

EXERCISE

Reconnection with the Body

This is one of the exercises you did in group to help you explore your connection to your own body. Periodically try to practice this exercise so that it becomes easier for you to focus on the four basic sensations: temperature, pressure, texture, moisture. You can also use this exercise (eyes open) as a grounding exercise.

> First, if you are comfortable, close your eyes. . . . Then slowly touch your face, arm, or hand. . . . See if you can focus mentally on its temperature. . . . Is it warm or cold? . . . Then focus on the pressure of your touch. . . . Is it light or firm? . . . Then focus on the texture . . . smooth or rough? . . . Finally, focus on the presence or absence of moisture. . . . Is it absolutely dry, or is there some moisture?

> Just try to relax into the sensations that you are feeling.

> Open your eyes. What was your experience of connecting with your body?

> Was it difficult? Was it easy?

What feelings did you have as you did this exercise?

_____

_____

_____

_____

_____

HOMEWORK

TRAUMA IN OUR LIVES

Pick three experiences that you think might have been abusive: one from childhood, one from adolescence, and one from adulthood, if possible. If not, pick three from any time period.

In the boxes on page 21, list

     A. the event

     B. how life was before the event

     C. how life was after the event

     D. how you view the overall impact of these traumas in your life
       (Did the events impact your life? If so, how?)

You can use the five questions below if you are trying to decide if an event in your life was abusive.

     1. Was there full consent? Was there coercion?

     2. Was there an element of betrayal, loss of trust?

     3. Was there violence, pain, restriction, force, or bodily harm?

     4. Did it feel like abuse to you?

     5. Did you feel afraid?

This exercise can help you see your strengths, resiliency, and survival skills.

It is important to remember that any memories you visit are in the past. Any feelings you have are part of the process of healing, and right now you are safe. You can use your safety symbol (session 1, page 7) and your grounding exercise (session 2, page 12) to help you, if you need them.

	CHILD	ADOLESCENT	ADULT
A. Event			
B. Life before the event			
C. Life after the event			
D. Overall impact of the traumatic events			

REFLECTION

What was the most meaningful part of the session for you?

_____

_____

_____

_____

_____

_____

SESSION 4

How Trauma Impacts Our Lives

Trauma can impact our lives in many ways. After a traumatic event, many women say they feel they are "losing control" of their lives. Often, these feelings of loss of control that come from the event can affect many parts of your life. You may reexperience the traumatic incident in your memories, thoughts, and dreams. These reexperienced traumas can be so intense that it feels as though the event is happening all over again. When this is happening, some women find it hard to concentrate and keep their minds on a task or action they are doing—even something as simple as watching TV. This can often add to feeling out of control. In reaction to a traumatic incident in your life, you may also have feelings of guilt; your self-image may change; or you may experience depression, a sense of isolation, and sadness. Fear and anxiety may be a part of each day. These are common reactions of women who have experienced trauma.

"In my dreams I'd see and feel the past

as though it were happening now. I'd wake up afraid

and wanting to run away as fast as I could.

I just thought I was going crazy."

What Is a Trigger?

A *trigger* is something that sets off a physical or emotional reaction in a person. It can be a sound, another person, a place, a smell, a behavior—almost anything that reminds you of the past trauma.

Women react to trauma on several different levels. Sometimes the reactions are physical. Physical reactions are automatic and happen without our control. For example, when faced with danger, our bodies automatically respond with a fight or flight response. The body can react as though it is reliving the traumatic events of the past. The body returns to what it knows about the past trauma. As you read earlier, if you are a woman in the criminal justice system, you may be triggered by being restrained, handcuffed, or searched by staff. This may remind you of abusive experiences in your past.

Impact on Relationships

It can be difficult to maintain relationships when you are feeling the effects of trauma or are reexperiencing the trauma. Here are some of the relationship problems that women often struggle with:

- idealizing or overvaluing relationships
- fear of commitment
- self-imposed isolation
- triangulating with others
- humiliating interactions
- involvement in abusive or criticizing relationships
- difficulty trusting self or others with intimacy
- tolerating patterns of abuse or excessive neediness
- emotional and physical caretaking of others at expense of self

(For more information, see *Leaving the Enchanted Forest: The Path from Relationship Addiction to Intimacy* by Stephanie Covington and Liana Beckett.)

Impact on Sexuality

Your sexuality may be impacted by the trauma. This may be true whether or not the trauma involved sexual abuse. These are some of the things that women talk about:

- avoidance of or fear of sex
- approaching sex as obligation
- negative feelings with touch
- difficulty with arousal, sensation
- vaginal pain
- emotional distance during sex (spacing out)
- disturbing sexual thoughts and images
- compulsive or inappropriate sexual behavior
- difficulty in intimate relationships

(For more information, see *Awakening Your Sexuality: A Guide for Recovering Women* by Stephanie Covington.)

▶ Here's a place to write about your relationships or any other concerns you may have.

_____

_____

_____

_____

_____

_____

_____

_____

_____

HOMEWORK

DRAWING YOUR COLLAGE

In your group session, you made a collage of words and images that show the impact of violence, abuse, and trauma in your life.

> Draw a small picture of your collage. Write your thoughts about what it means to you.

Review the trauma chart that you did in the last session (page 21) to see if there is anything else to add to it now that you have explored new information in this session.

REFLECTION

What is the one thing you would like to remember from this session?

_____

_____

_____

_____

_____

_____

The Addiction and Trauma Connection: Spirals of Recovery and Healing

Addiction and trauma are often connected in women's lives. Some women self-medicate by using substances to numb themselves and avoid the effects of trauma. Women who abuse alcohol and other drugs are also more vulnerable to traumatic situations. In addition, many women grew up in homes where there was both substance abuse and interpersonal violence.

Often women believe that alcohol and other drugs can help them to

- make connections with others
- comfort themselves
- manage or avoid feelings
- escape physical pain
- ease social withdrawal
- create distance
- build courage
- increase hope, make the world seem better
- forget the past
- increase a sense of vitality
- feel comfortable with sexual intimacy
- dissociate (achieve an altered state)
- feel numb
- rewire the brain
- maintain the status quo

The Upward Spiral: A Transformational Model

There are some similarities in the ways that trauma and addiction can impact your life. The spiral is one way of looking at this.

In the Spiral of Addiction and Recovery, a downward spiral represents what happens when a woman is addicted. Her life becomes narrower and narrower. The line through the middle represents her drug of choice, and she organizes her life around it. Then there is a turning point and she steps onto a new path—recovery. The upward spiral represents recovery. Here her life is growing and expanding with new interests and new relationships.

Spiral of Addiction and Recovery
(Transformation)

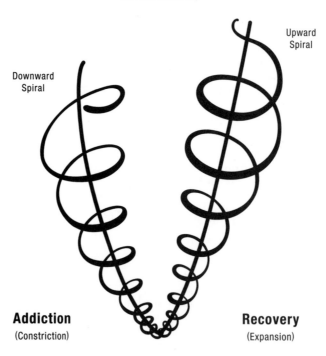

Downward Spiral

Upward Spiral

Addiction
(Constriction)

Recovery
(Expansion)

(Adapted from *Helping Women Recover.* Copyright 1999 by S. Covington. This material is used by permission of John Wiley & Sons, Inc.)

You can use the same concept of a spiral and apply it to trauma. Trauma often limits a woman's life. The traumatic event(s) in her life can become a central issue for her (as represented by the line through the middle of the downward spiral). Again, there is a turning point at the bottom of the downward spiral. The upward spiral can also represent the process of healing from trauma. As you become more aware of how trauma has impacted your life, you will experience less constriction and limitation. With new behaviors and coping skills, there is greater opportunity for growth and expansion. While the trauma is still a thread that runs through your life, it is no longer the core. In both upward spirals—Recovery and Healing—a profound internal shift takes place when a woman moves to the upward spiral. Something transformational happens.

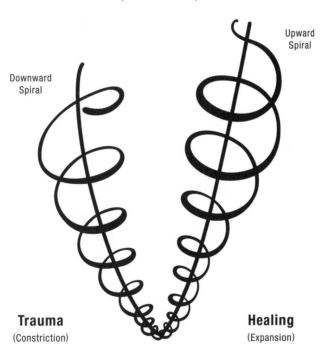

Spiral of Trauma and Healing

(Transformation)

Downward
Spiral

Upward
Spiral

Trauma
(Constriction)

Healing
(Expansion)

(Adapted from *Helping Women Recover*. Copyright 1999 by S. Covington. This material is used by permission of John Wiley & Sons, Inc.)

EXERCISE

MY OWN SPIRAL

The spiral can help you to understand both the impact of addiction and trauma on your life and the process of recovery and healing.

1. List things that limit (narrow, constrict) your life. For example, abusive relationships, abuse of alcohol and other drugs, isolation, shame—anything that holds you back from living the life you want to lead.

2. List things that *expand* your life. For example, a support group, talking to a counselor, sobriety, sharing your story with a trusted friend, trying new things.

3. Where do you think you are on the spirals? Are you on the upward spiral moving toward expansion and recovery/healing or on the downward spiral, feeling more constricted by traumatic events and/or addiction? Or, are you somewhere in between?

_____

_____

_____

_____

_____

_____

_____

4. Think about one way you feel limited, held back, or constricted in your life today. What will it take to make that limitation or constriction change and begin to open up the spiral toward expansion?

_____

_____

_____

_____

_____

_____

Safety

Safety is the first step and a core element in healing from trauma. This includes both physical and emotional safety.

E X E R C I S E

PHYSICAL AND EMOTIONAL SAFETY

Answering these questions will help you identify what makes you feel safe and unsafe. Keep in mind that there are no right or wrong answers. Each woman is entitled to her feelings, needs, and concerns about safety.

1. What are some things you do to feel safe in your life?

_____

_____

_____

_____

2. What does emotional safety mean to you?

_____

_____

_____

_____

3. When and where do you feel emotionally safe?

_____

_____

4. When and where do you feel emotionally unsafe?

_____

_____

5. What is physical safety, and what do you do to keep physically safe?

EXERCISE

DRAWING SAFETY

In the space below draw what came to your mind in the group exercise—images, thoughts, feelings. Your drawing does not have to be artistic; just draw what safety means to you.

Self-Care

In your group, you discussed safety with others and what safety means to you. A key part of safety is safety with ourselves. One way you can develop safety with yourself is through self-care. Self-care is a range of behaviors that includes everything from what you eat and personal hygiene to valuing yourself and acknowledging your feelings. How you take care of yourself is very important. When we are doing a good job of caring for ourselves, we are at less risk for self-destructive behavior (substance abuse, unsafe sex, and so on).

The Self-Care Scale is a tool you can use to see areas in which you are taking care of yourself effectively and areas you may want to work on.

E X E R C I S E

SELF-CARE SCALE

Please take a few moments to look at the following fifteen items and determine the degree to which you do the following. Put an X on the line to show where you think you are on the scale. This is only for you to see, and no one will judge how well you are doing.

	Not at all	Just a little	Pretty much	Very much
1. I keep up my physical appearance (nails, hair, bathing, clean clothes).				
2. I exercise regularly.				
3. I eat healthy meals.				
4. I get restful sleep.				
5. I go to work/school (or complete tasks).				
6. I can adapt to change.				

	Not at all	Just a little	Pretty much	Very much
7. I keep up my living space.				
8. I take constructive criticism well.				
9. I can accept praise.				
10. I laugh at funny things.				
11. I acknowledge my needs and feelings.				
12. I engage in new interests.				
13. I can relax without drugs and alcohol.				
14. I value myself.				
15. I live a clean and sober life.				

(Adapted from *Helping Women Recover.* Copyright 1999 by S. Covington. This material is used by permission of John Wiley & Sons, Inc.)

HOMEWORK

Your homework assignment is to focus on self-care, identifying your obstacles to self-care and the areas of self-care you would like to enhance in your own life. See if there is one area of self-care that needs attention and that you would like to work on. Over the next few days, also be aware of how you feel in your environment.

1. What is the one area of self-care you plan to focus your attention on?

_____

_____

_____

2. What are your personal barriers to better self-care?

_____

_____

_____

_____

3. Take a few minutes to think about your environment. What helps to make you feel safe, comfortable, secure, and supported?

_____

_____

_____

_____

REFLECTION

Use this space to write or draw about your experience in this group session.

Grounding and Self-Soothing

Grounding techniques are strategies to help you stay present in the "here and now." They can be very helpful if you dissociate (become emotionally absent and "lose time"). When women experience trauma, they often feel like they lose their grounding and centering. It is important to reestablish ground so you cannot be easily knocked off balance by your emotions and reactions.

In your group meeting, you did some exercises on self-soothing and relaxation. Grounding yourself can be a valuable tool for healing and recovery.

EXERCISE

GROUNDING

Do these exercises slowly and respectfully. If at any time you find the exercise disturbing or feel emotions build up inside of you, stop and let things settle. As you learn to maintain a focus on your external environment, internal emotional pain will begin to diminish. You can also write or draw about the emotions that come up for you.

Exercise 1

Stand and feel your feet on the ground.

Notice the springiness in your legs. Feel the way your feet connect with the ground, almost like a magnet is holding you there or a tree with big, strong roots. With your feet firmly planted, sway slowly from side to side from the ankles, then forward and backward. This will help you find your center of gravity. It is usually located in the upper pelvic area.

As you continue to sway, place your hands on your lower belly and sense your center of gravity.

Now, sit back in your chair. Relax. Be sure that your feet are firmly on the ground. Place your hands on your lower belly again and feel the energy coming into that area through your feet. What do you feel?

Exercise 2

Another exercise is "belly breathing." Lie on your back (or you can sit in a chair) with one hand on your chest and one on your stomach. Most people find that they primarily breathe from their chest. You can tell when your hand on your chest moves up and down. Try moving your breath deeper into your lower belly so that your hand on your stomach begins to move up and down. Blow the air out of your mouth, rather than your nose, and let your belly fill with air.

Exercise 3

Sit in a comfortable position with your feet on the floor. Concentrate on your breathing—the breathing in, the pause, the breathing out. Feel your body expand from the center and release back toward the center. With each breath, breathe a little deeper, moving deeper down into your abdomen. As you breathe in, take in "good things" (self-love, hope, courage, joy) and as you breathe out, let go of things you do not want in your life (self-criticism, stress, fear). Do this for two to three minutes.

Exercise 4

Another way to feel grounded and centered is to walk without shoes, if weather and terrain permit (this may or may not be permissible in a correctional setting). In the park, in the woods, on the beach, on your favorite street, in your garden, or on the grass in your yard can all be good places to try this out. Breathe deeply and think about your feet as they connect with the ground. Look around and take in your surroundings. Be in the present and feel the connection with your world.

Here is a place to write or draw about your experience with these exercises.

Other Exercises

Here are some other exercises that you can use.

Some people feel grounded holding or lying down with an animal and listening to its heartbeat or the calmness in its breathing. Some find a grounded feeling by looking out at the large, vast sky and watching the clouds go by. Others find it in walking through nature and connecting with the universe through their feet as well as their senses. (Also see pages 12 and 19.)

When working through painful things, such as a past trauma, we all need to have ways to comfort or soothe ourselves without using alcohol or other drugs. It is helpful to know ways to comfort yourself without relying on temporary fixes that may, in fact, complicate your life.

Self-Soothing

Self-soothing is calming and comforting yourself. The following exercise can help you develop your self-soothing skills.

E X E R C I S E

SELF-SOOTHING CHART

This chart is divided into four squares, each representing a different situation. In each of the situations, you need ways to soothe yourself.

- What are some things you do to relax or "self-soothe" when you are alone in the daytime? (upper left-hand corner of box)

- What are some things you do to self-soothe when alone in the nighttime?

- What are some things you do to self-soothe during the day when you are with others?

- What are some things you do to self-soothe when you are with others in the nighttime?

	ALONE	WITH OTHERS
Daytime		
Nighttime		

(Adapted from *Helping Women Recover.* Copyright 1999 by S. Covington. This material is used by permission of John Wiley & Sons, Inc.)

Relaxation

Relaxation is one way to self-soothe. Learning how to calm yourself and relax when you have been bombarded by intense emotions is a self-soothing skill we all need to develop. This is one good way to take care of yourself.

EXERCISE

RELAXATION

Here is the relaxation exercise you did in your group. You can use this to calm or soothe yourself. You can use it at night, during the day, anytime you'd like. You may want to have a friend read it to you.

Lie on your back on the floor. If you would rather sit, that is fine, too. Close your eyes. (If you feel too uncomfortable with your eyes closed, then keep them open and focus on an object.) Take a deep breath in while you silently count to four: one . . . two . . . three . . . four. Now breathe out slowly: one . . . two . . . three . . . four. Try to breathe from your abdomen, not just from your chest. Breathe in again. And out again. Now, repeat that slow breathing two more times.

Now, in your mind, I want you to picture your favorite safe place to be. Maybe you are walking in a beautiful park or garden. Maybe you are getting cozy in your favorite chair or in your bed. Maybe you are lying in the sun or boating on the water. Picture that place in your mind and imagine yourself there. Keep breathing deeply and very slowly. Starting with your head and working down your body like a scan, let your muscles relax. Let your forehead relax. Let your cheekbones relax. Let your jaw joints relax. Let your neck and upper shoulders relax. As you exhale, imagine all the tension going out with each breath. Let it go. Let your hands and arms go limp next to you. Let your chest, stomach, and whole middle part of your body relax. Keep breathing in and out. Let your hips, your buttocks, and your upper legs and lower legs relax. Let your feet and toes relax. Let your whole body relax. Breathe in and out. Keep imagining that safe place you selected. Enjoy where you are; enjoy the tension going out of your body. Be relaxed, almost floating and weightless, as you stay in that image.

Now open your eyes. How do you feel right now? Do you feel more relaxed?

This is a self-soothing technique that you can do when you feel stressed or anxious. Using your breath and remembering to breathe deeply can be an important skill.

Personal Boundaries—Like a Zipper

Developing personal boundaries is another skill that can help you feel centered, grounded, and more in control of your life.

In order to create strong, caring relationships, it is important for you not only to know when and how to set clear limits with other people but also to accept and honor the boundaries and limits set by them. Personal boundaries are based on your upbringing, culture, and experience with others.

It is best to determine your boundaries on your own internal compass, not on your reaction to external things or people. One way to think about boundaries is like "zippers." Imagine that you have a zipper around you. When the zipper tab is on the outside, others can move it at will. If it is on the inside, you can control it.

It can be empowering to set and regulate your own boundaries, but it is not always easy to do so. Communicating clearly what your limits are with strangers, family members, or friends is an important first step. Other people cannot guess your boundaries. Some people will try to test them or use their own comfort level as the standard for others. Therefore, it is important to tell them when you feel comfortable or uncomfortable.

HOMEWORK

1. Think about your boundaries and write or draw about situations and times when you felt comfortable.

2. Think about your boundaries and write or draw about situations and times when you felt uncomfortable.

3. Also, try some grounding and self-soothing exercises before your next group meeting. Here's a place to record how you felt before and after each exercise.

REFLECTION

Here's a place where you can write your thoughts and feelings about the group, your
week, and your life.

_____

_____

_____

_____

_____

_____

_____

If you have a photograph of yourself as a young girl (one to ten years old), please bring
it to the next session.

SESSION 7

Abuse and the Family

Relationships are one of the most important factors that shape who we are. For most of us, the most influential relationships are the ones we had as children. Those family relationships established patterns for how we relate to ourselves and to others. Many women come from families in which their needs were not met. They took on roles in an effort to meet their needs and to survive in emotionally empty or emotionally challenging environments.

In this session, you explored some of the ways that family members can interact with each other. By doing a family sculpture, you began to think about your family and your role(s) in the family. Many women have their first experience of abuse in their home. In abusive homes, many children may try to become invisible in order to avoid punishment; the mask of an approved role provides protective cover. In the last session, we discussed personal boundaries. In the exercise that demonstrated family dynamics, you saw how family helps shape our physical and emotional boundaries.

Roles in the Family

▶ What are some things you learned from the Family Sculpture exercise about roles in the family?

_____

_____

_____

_____

Families and Abuse

A high-stress family is at risk for abuse. Many women do not know that they have been abused because they assume the behavior in their family is normal. As we discussed in an earlier session (see page 15), there are various forms of abuse, including physical, sexual, and emotional abuse. One type of abuse is *domestic violence*. It is defined as any exploitive or threatening behavior intended to harm or exert power over another family or household member. Sexual abuse is another form of abuse found in families. Remember, the important indicators for abuse in the family are behaviors that either threaten or use people and intentions or motives to harm or exert power over others.

Below is a copy of the Sexual Abuse in Families continuum that you discussed in your group.

Sexual Abuse in Families

Psychological Abuse	*Covert Abuse*	*Overt Abuse*
Sexual jokes	Inappropriate touching	Exhibitionism
Verbal harassment	Voyeurism	French kissing
Violating boundaries	Ridicule of body	Fondling
Telling child inappropriate sexual information	Sexual hugs	Oral sex
	Pornography	Penetration

(Adapted from *Helping Women Recover.* Copyright 1999 by S. Covington. This material is used by permission of John Wiley & Sons, Inc.)

This will help you to see the range of behaviors in a family that can harm a child. At one end of the continuum are behaviors that can be confusing because they are subtle and hard to recognize as abusive at the time that they occur. Covert abuse is also subtle but it can leave a girl or woman with a distinct feeling of discomfort and questioning what has happened. It's easier to see and understand how overt sexual behaviors are abusive to a child.

When abuse takes place within the family, it can be "crazy making" for the victims because the people who tell them "I love you" are also their abusers. It breaks down their sense of trust, safety, and security in the world because they may not know if they are safe even within their intimate circle.

Your "Inner Child"

Even though you are now an adult, it is important to realize that you have an "inner child" inside of you no matter how old you are or what your growing-up experience was like. Many of us have not taken the time to look within to see what this child is thinking, doing, feeling, or saying to us.

Our inner child, or that little girl inside of each of us, is that unique core self that we each possess who is the essence of our true self. The inner child is that part that is most natural, creative, playful, and innocent. It can also be a place where we hold on to childhood trauma and scars.

It is when you go within yourself to reclaim your neglected or hurt inner child that you can deal most effectively with your past trauma and the outer world.

(For more information, see *Growing Up Again: Parenting Ourselves, Parenting Our Children* by Jean Illsley Clarke and Connie Dawson).

⌒

"When I closed my eyes and went inside myself, I found a little girl

about six or seven years old. She was in a house with no windows or doors,

just empty rooms. She was running frantically from room to room trying

to find someone. There was no one there. She was all alone."

HOMEWORK

DESCRIBING YOUR INNER CHILD

In the group exercise, you visualized your inner child. You thought about your childhood when you were between one and ten years old, and you visualized the place where you lived. You also explored and thought about this time in your life by answering the following questions: What was your room like? What was the color of the floor or the walls? Did you have a nickname? Did you have any pets? What were your favorite foods? Who were your best friends? What did you like to do with your best friends? What scared you? Did you have any secrets? What made you laugh? What did you want to do when you grew up?

Do you have a sense of your inner child's age? Feelings? Usual state of mind? Needs? Wants? What does that child need from you now?

In the space below, list all that you know about your inner child. Then you can create a reparenting plan that suits her age and her needs.

For example:

Age:_____

Where you lived: _____

Nickname: _____

Favorite foods: _____

Best friends: _____

_____

Feelings: _____

Other: _____

_____

_____

_____

_____

What else do you know about your inner child? Your childhood?

_____

_____

_____

_____

_____

HOMEWORK

INNER CHILD REPARENTING PLAN

Without meeting the needs of your inner child, it can be difficult to meet your adult needs and have healthy relationships with those around you. Like any child, your inner child will continue to protest loudly until her needs are met. It is important to take the time to give yourself/your inner child the attention that she did not receive in childhood. Attunement to your inner child can be a first step toward love and healing.

In the space below, draw or describe how you would "reparent" your inner child.

	WHAT YOU CAN DO NOW
Your inner child's needs	
Your inner child's wants	
What your inner child needs from you now	

One way to find out about your inner child's needs and wants is to visualize her again in your mind. When you get a clear picture of her, ask what she needs and wants. Pick one need your inner child has and try to meet that need this week.

50

REFLECTION

What was the most meaningful part of the session for you?

_____

_____

_____

_____

_____

_____

_____

Mind and Body Connection

We know that traumatic events impact us in a variety of ways. We may have been so overwhelmed during the traumatic event that we couldn't understand or process what was happening. These unprocessed, emotionally charged bits of trauma can be stored in our memory and in our bodies.

Trauma can result in a disconnection between memory and feeling. Some women have memories without feeling, and some have feelings without memory. One of the most important parts of healing is getting the feelings and the memories connected and expressed. This is part of the mind-body connection. When the feelings from the traumatic event are not expressed, they are stored and often expressed later through the body.

Emotional Wellness

Trauma can profoundly impact your emotional development. Addiction also impacts emotional development. A woman may be unaccustomed to having feelings. She may have shut down emotionally after a traumatic experience ("psychic numbing") and may need help finding the words to name how she feels. Then she may need to learn both expression and containment. *Containment* means having the ability to hold or contain a feeling until you want to express it. There are other women who are overwhelmed and flooded by feelings; they need to learn expression and containment, too. When you can express and contain feelings, then they no longer control you.

The following five steps can help you begin to create emotional wellness in your life.

Five Steps to Emotional Wellness

1. Become aware of when and how you are feeling. Tune in to yourself.

2. Try to locate the feeling in your body. Where are you experiencing the sensations?

3. Name the feeling—label it.

4. Express the feeling.

5. Learn to contain the feeling.

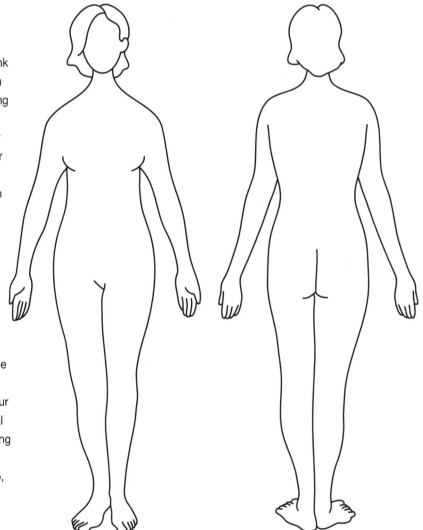

E X E R C I S E

FEELINGS AND THE BODY

1. Start by closing your eyes. Relax. Breathe deeply. Think about your body and begin to notice what you are feeling now. See if you can sense where the feeling is in your body. Also notice how your face feels (the sensations you have in your face) when you are having a feeling.

2. Open your eyes. Using colored pencils, show on the diagram to the right where the feeling is located in your body. Also draw your facial expression. If you are having difficulty, be patient with yourself. This is hard to do, but it will get easier with practice.

3. Now let's do this exercise a little differently. From the Examples of Feelings list below, pick a feeling that you have felt in the past week, or pick a feeling you have often (you can choose a feeling that isn't on the list). Find a different colored pencil and mark on the diagram where you felt that feeling in your body.

   For instance, if you picked mad or angry, think about your body. Perhaps your heart raced, your face turned red, or you began to sweat.

EXAMPLES OF FEELINGS

Anger	Happy	Calm	Disgusted
Joy	Fear	Lonely	Surprised
Sad	Amused	Mad	Guilt
Anxious	Hurt	Contented	Excitement
Thoughtful	Bitter	Miserable	Pride
Nervous	Jealous	Disappointed	Shame
Depressed	Relieved	Glad	Tired
Grateful	Disturbed	Embarrassed	Lost

Here are some tips if a feeling is overwhelming you:

1. Slow down or even stop what you are doing.

2. Ask yourself, "What am I feeling?" Try to name the feeling.

3. Ask yourself, "Does the intensity of this feeling match the situation?" Give yourself some time to sort this out.

4. Then ask yourself, "As I have this feeling, how old am I?" (Is my inner child having this feeling?)

If you are feeling overwhelmed, it is possible that your "inner child" is connected to the feeling. If the intensity of the feeling does not match the current situation, or you feel younger than your current age, the feeling is probably connected to the past.

HOMEWORK

1. **Feelings and the Body diagram:** Continue to use the Feelings and the Body diagram on page 52. Use a different colored pencil or crayon for each feeling you have. Practice locating the feeling in your body.

2. **Containment:** The zipper is a useful way of thinking about containment (we also discussed the zipper as a boundary on page 42). If you are flooded or overwhelmed by feelings, try to visualize having a zipper that allows you to close up your feelings and contain them. You can unzip the zipper when you want to express your feelings.

3. In the space below, write or draw about one experience of containing your feelings.

REFLECTION

What is one thing you want to remember about this session?

_____

_____

_____

_____

_____

The World of Feelings

Some people believe that there are six basic, universal human emotions—anger, sadness, fear, happiness, disgust, and surprise. And then there are lots of other feelings that are secondary—such as guilt, pride, jealousy, and excitement. Expression and containment of feelings are both very important skills to learn. They might seem simple at first, since there are so few basic emotions. Yet these are actually complicated tasks for many people—especially trauma survivors and recovering alcoholics and addicts.

It is essential to remember that expression and containment can only be learned with time and practice. There are many feelings that you may have but have not shared with others—or at the other end of the continuum, you may have felt "flooded" by feelings that could not be contained. Expression and containment can be difficult when emotions arise immediately.

"The group has been hard for me. It brought up a lot of anger

and pain, perhaps even grief. Feelings I could never express.

But it was worth it. I've never valued myself as a woman.

But now I can. Truly awesome discovery and so simple."

EXERCISE

THE OBSERVER SELF

The Observer Self is a part of you that can help with containment. Many of us become overly reactive—we respond quickly and abruptly to other people's words and actions. The observer part of your self is that part that is capable of seeing reality without judging. It is the part that is a witness, not a judge. With practice, you can develop this part of yourself.

In your group, you picked a situation you have been in recently where there was a problem and you experienced a lot of feelings. You closed your eyes and got totally involved in the scene of the problem. You focused on this situation.

The following are directions for you to practice this exercise on your own.

> Again, pick a situation and close your eyes. (You may want to have a friend read this to you again. In time, you will be able to do it from memory.) Be aware of how you are feeling as you involve yourself in this situation. . . . Notice the look on your face. . . . Notice the faces of others around you. . . . Notice how you move your body. . . . Notice the energy around you. . . . Just feel this experience for a moment as though it is happening right now. Now, leave the situation and move to a spot above it. . . . Look down on the scene you have just left behind and see it in its entirety. . . . Notice what you are doing. . . . Notice how others are reacting to you. . . . Look at the roles you and others are playing out. . . . Look at the place this is happening . . . the city, the community, the culture you live in.
>
> Now, very slowly go back into the scene again. Totally immerse yourself back into the center of it. Allow yourself to stay there for a few seconds. Be aware of how your body feels.
>
> Allow this scene to come to an end in whatever way you wish to resolve it for now.

When you open your eyes, you'll want to ask yourself the following questions:

1. How did it feel to be totally in the situation?

    _____

    _____

    _____

2. How did it feel to be observing it?

    _____

    _____

    _____

3. Did you notice the difference in your body between being in the situation and being out of it? Explain.

    _____

    _____

    _____

Most women feel better when using the Observer Self. Learning and practicing the Observer Self will help in developing containment as well as learning more about yourself.

This is also a way to practice detachment. Detachment allows you to be less reactive. This is different from dissociation. With dissociation, you are disconnected and lost or split off from what is happening—removed from reality. With the Observer Self—or detachment— you are very present, developing and using more awareness and consciousness, not less. The Observer Self is a part of your strength, and using it empowers you.

Three Common Feelings

There are many feelings that women who have been abused share. Some of them are anger, loss, and shame.

Anger

Sometimes women are angry at their abusers or at a person who did not protect them (in some cases, their mothers). Sometimes they turn their anger inward, if they cannot express it, and become depressed. Some anger may come out in self-harming behavior (cutting or burning). And in some cases, anger is covering up another feeling, like fear. Fear or sadness can be underneath anger.

► What are some ways that you express anger?

_____

_____

_____

_____

"I know now that I bottled up my feelings for so long that

every time I felt anything, I used anger to cover it up."

"A lot of women who are incarcerated lose their children, their

homes, and their relationships. You also lose a lot of self-respect."

Loss

Loss and grief are common experiences for women who have been abused, who have substance abuse problems, or who are in the criminal justice system. Some women have had multiple losses—of their children, their family members, their childhood innocence, or their health.

EXERCISE

LOSSES

1. Think back on your life and the losses you have experienced. How have these losses affected you?

2. What are some ways that you have grieved your losses?

"The down side to being in jail is not being with my children and not being able to enjoy the things I like to do. Things like going shopping and being able to work. There are many things in our lives that we take for granted, and I hope when things start going too fast that I slow down and take a good look around. I have lost a lot and watched many other women lose a lot more."

Shame

Many women experience shame. When women are abused as children or as adults, they often feel ashamed and believe somehow it was their fault. Substance-abusing women often feel shame because of the stigma society places on addicted women.

Shame is when a woman feels there is something wrong or bad about her. *Guilt* is when she feels there is something wrong or bad about her behavior. Shame can become a very destructive core issue. This is a deep-seated feeling, the roots of which can be difficult to unearth.

▶ How has shame impacted your life?

_____

_____

_____

_____

_____

_____

_____

"I felt like there was something deep inside of me that was really bad. I could imagine myself having something inside of me that I just couldn't get out. This feeling I think came from my parents because I took on so much shame because of their addictions. I was always embarrassed about where I came from, and then later I was in an abusive relationship. I had a hard time getting over the fact that I didn't leave that relationship sooner, even though when I look at my upbringing, I can see why."

Empathy and Compassion

Empathy and compassion are important feelings to develop. *Empathy* is the ability to share in another's feelings and emotions. Some of us seem to have empathy naturally, and others do not. Developing the feeling of empathy enables us to be more *compassionate*. This is when we sense the suffering or trouble of another person and we want to help. It is important for our relationships to learn to feel empathy and compassion. It is also important for you to feel compassion for yourself and the pain you have suffered.

▶ How do you show empathy to others and compassion to yourself?

_____

_____

_____

_____

_____

_____

_____

_____

"My heart and my eyes opened up.

I really didn't realize that women were physically

and sexually abused so much.

I pray for them every day."

✖

MEETING A FEELING

In your group session, you picked a feeling that you have often, or one that you have had very recently, or one you would like to understand better. Then you did a guided exercise that took you to your inner self, and in that place you found your feeling.

1. Draw a picture of that feeling—it may be a specific shape, design, or symbol.

2. What did you learn from the feeling? What does it do for you? What does it need from you?

_____

_____

_____

_____

_____

_____

_____

_____

HOMEWORK

Using page 56 (with Observer Self directions), practice two Observer Self situations. After each situation, ask yourself if you felt any empathy or compassion in these situations. Write about these two Observer Self situations, noting empathy and compassion.

_____

_____

_____

_____

_____

_____

_____

_____

REFLECTION

This is a place for you to write or draw about your experience in this group—maybe it's the one thing you want to remember from this group.

Duplicating this page is illegal. Do not copy this material without written permission from the publisher.

63

Healthy Relationships:
Wheel of Love

In the past sessions, we looked at where we have been in our lives by examining our families of origin, understanding our trauma experiences and responses to them, learning relaxation and self-soothing techniques, identifying boundaries, and regaining our ability to feel and trust our feelings. We are now focusing on creating healthy relationships in our lives. In your group, you discussed the steps to a healthy relationship.

Developing Healthy Relationships

A healthy relationship is one where each person

1. feels a greater sense of zest, vitality, and energy. For example, you spend time with a friend, and when you part, you feel energized and alive. This happens because you are both putting energy into the relationship—and the energy is moving between you. Several days later you meet a friend, and afterward you feel depleted and exhausted. This may have happened because you were giving (providing energy to the relationship), and your friend was just taking.

2. feels more able to act and does act. A healthy relationship empowers you to act, and you feel free to take action in your life.

3. has a more accurate perception of herself and the other person. Because I am in this relationship with you, I see parts of myself that I would not see or know if I were alone.

4. feels a greater sense of self-worth. I feel good about myself in this relationship with you.

5. feels more connected to the other person and feels a greater motivation for connections with other people beyond those in this specific relationship. As time goes on, I feel more and more connected to you, and I also feel a desire to have friends and be connected to others (Miller 1986, 1990).

Here is a picture of the Relationship Wheel. Respect, mutuality, and compassion are at the center. They are the core of healthy relationships.

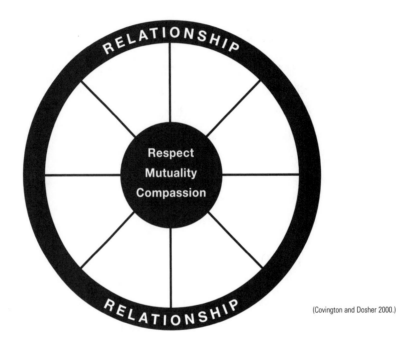

(Covington and Dosher 2000.)

- *Respect* is the appreciation of someone's values, and it begins to happen when we see that person's integrity. We often earn respect when we are willing to do the "right thing" or take the "right action," particularly when the choice is difficult.

- *Mutuality* means there is an equal investment in the relationship. Each person has a willingness and desire to see the other as well as be seen, to hear the other as well as be heard, and to respect the other's vulnerability as well as be vulnerable. Mutuality also means that there is an awareness of the "we," not a sole focus on two "I's."

- *Compassion* is similar to empathy, but it occurs on a deeper level. Empathy is understanding others' feelings and being able to feel with them. Compassion means that we go a step further and join with them in their struggle or pain. When we are compassionate, we lend ourselves to another's process—we give of ourselves in order to be with the other emotionally.

Steps to a Healthy Relationship

The following are some of the steps toward creating a healthy relationship:

Similarities

Similarities of temperament and shared interests between partners are certainly desirable, important, and fun. However, some of the more important similarities are the role of the relationship in each person's life and a shared vision of the future. Support for sobriety is also a crucial similarity when one or both of the partners is committed to recovery.

Ability to Deal with Change

Life is always changing, requiring us to change and adapt along with it. Because people do change, their needs and perspectives on life are also bound to change over time. In love relationships, the changing needs of one of the partners can cause a major relationship conflict. Therefore, the ability to deal effectively with change is a crucial skill in relationships.

Compatible Values

Some couples never discussed or paid attention to each other's values when they met. When a relationship moves into any kind of depth, values inevitably come into play. Discussing values, however, is not enough. People's *real* values are reflected in how they live and what they do, rather than just what they say. Learning about people's values by observation takes time.

Effective, Open Communication

Good communication is fundamental to all human relationships. The clarity of intent behind the message is one key to being understood. When a speaker is not aware of her or his motives or is not clear about her or his intent when speaking, and when words or body language don't fit the context, then the result is a mixed message. Good, clear communication can reduce conflict by eliminating needless misunderstandings or building of resentments.

Duplicating this page is illegal. Do not copy this material without written permission from the publisher.

67

Effective Conflict/Anger Resolution

The closer the love relationship, the more individual differences become evident—and the greater the possibility of conflict. Not only are differences to be expected, but they can be wonderful assets in a relationship. Differences may also become challenges, particularly if there is no open communication, and negotiation skills are lacking. Anger is not necessarily negative, as long as it is clear, is confined to an "I" statement that expresses an individual's feeling of frustration, and bears no threat of violence.

Effective Negotiation

Negotiation is at the heart of conflict resolution through problem solving. One way to think about negotiation is in terms of needs and wants. Needs are essential things that a person has to have; wants are preferences. In a relationship, one person's needs should have preference over the other person's wants. Another way to negotiate is to think about what the relationship needs versus what each individual may need or want.

Firm Personal Boundaries

People have physical, emotional, and intellectual boundaries that can be violated in different ways. In order to create a strong love relationship, it is important for each person not only to know when and how to set clear limits but also to accept and honor the boundaries and limits set by the partner. Ideally, personal boundaries are based on your own internal cues, not on a reaction to external triggers.

Healthy Sexual Expression

Healthy sexuality is a source of sensual and physical pleasure. It can be an expression of trust, of love, of tenderness, of fondness, of creativity, of playfulness. Sexuality is a powerful form of communication. It is important for partners to identify what they communicate or—more commonly—what they *don't* communicate to each other about sex. Building a climate of intimacy in which they feel free to express their sensuality and sexuality with each other is crucial.

Shared Quality Time

The issue of time is not a simple formula. In our demanding world, there can be vast differences between the time needs and the time availability of two partners. At its best, quality time is leisure time, open-ended, without built-in schedules or endings. It is time in which events, communication, and activities are allowed to unfold at their own pace, without a specific agenda. It requires nothing except a couple's willingness to be with each other openly, accepting and allowing whatever comes.

Friendship

Friendship is the cornerstone of intimate relationships. Friendship certainly is not a precondition for starting an intimate love relationship. And yet it is hard to imagine that over time a relationship could evolve into a healthy, successful, loving partnership without developing a strong element of friendship (Covington and Beckett 1988).

The Power and Control Wheel and the Relationship Wheel

In an earlier session, we discussed the Power and Control Wheel, where power and control are at the center of violent, abusive relationships.

1. What do you think about or feel when you look at these different wheels?

_____

_____

_____

_____

Power and Control Wheel

(Duluth Domestic Abuse Intervention Project, 202 East Superior Street, Duluth, MN 55802.)

Relationship Wheel
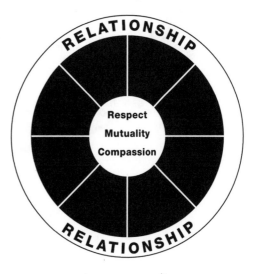
(Covington and Dosher 2000.)

Here is a reminder of the abusive behaviors in violent relationships where power and control are at the center.

Power and Control Wheel

(Duluth Domestic Abuse Intervention Project,
202 East Superior Street, Duluth, MN 55802.)

Now you have an opportunity to fill in the spokes of this relationship wheel to create a relationship based on respect, mutuality, and compassion. What would you want in your relationship?

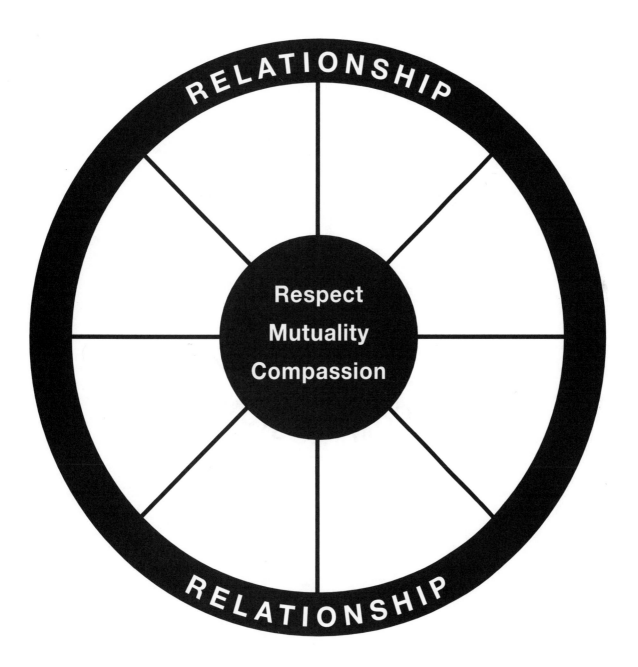

(Covington and Dosher 2000.)

Wheel of Love

Love is created by respect, mutuality, and compassion. Love is both a feeling and a behavior.

Wheel of Love

(Covington and Dosher 2000.)

HOMEWORK

THE RELATIONSHIP SCALE

The steps to healthy relationships we have talked about are by no means limited to romantic-love partnerships. They are important for any relationship that holds the promise of openness and intimacy—including friendship.

1. Think about one of your current relationships (it does not need to be sexual).

2. Next, circle the number on the scale that shows where you rate your relationship now; your rating should be based on specific behaviors or situations. The number 1 represents the low end of the scale and 10 represents the high end.

3. Mark with an arrow the place on the scale where you want your relationship to be.

4. Finally, choose one item from the list that for you is a top priority. Think about what you can do to change this in your relationship, and consider discussing your wish with your partner.

1. Similarities

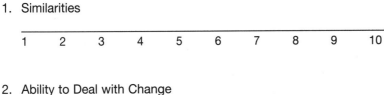

```
1    2    3    4    5    6    7    8    9    10
```

2. Ability to Deal with Change

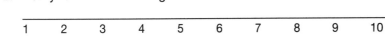

```
1    2    3    4    5    6    7    8    9    10
```

3. Compatible Values

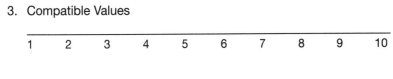

```
1    2    3    4    5    6    7    8    9    10
```

4. Effective, Open Communication

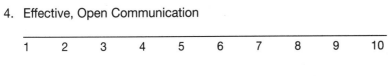

```
1    2    3    4    5    6    7    8    9    10
```

5. Effective Conflict/Anger Resolution

```
1    2    3    4    5    6    7    8    9    10
```

6. Effective Negotiation

| 1 | 2 | 3 | 4 | 5 | 6 | 7 | 8 | 9 | 10 |

7. Firm Personal Boundaries

| 1 | 2 | 3 | 4 | 5 | 6 | 7 | 8 | 9 | 10 |

8. Healthy Sexual Expression

| 1 | 2 | 3 | 4 | 5 | 6 | 7 | 8 | 9 | 10 |

9. Shared Quality Time

| 1 | 2 | 3 | 4 | 5 | 6 | 7 | 8 | 9 | 10 |

10. Friendship

| 1 | 2 | 3 | 4 | 5 | 6 | 7 | 8 | 9 | 10 |

(Adapted from *Leaving the Enchanted Forest: The Path from Relationship Addiction to Intimacy* by Stephanie Covington and Liana Beckett. 1988. HarperCollins Publishers.)

You may also want to continue filling in the "spokes" of your Relationship Wheel with the things that are important to you in a relationship.

HOMEWORK

LOVE IN YOUR LIFE

Continue to think about the love in your life. Keep working on your collage if you like. Or do something else creative, like writing a poem, drawing a picture, writing a song, or using clay to express your feelings about the love you have and want in your life.

Here's a place to sketch a picture of your collage.

REFLECTION

What is the one thing you want to remember from this session?

_____

_____

_____

_____

_____

_____

Please bring something that is special and important to you to the next session. It may be an actual object (e.g., a special stone) or something that represents or symbolizes what is important to you (e.g., a photograph or drawing). Also, please bring your love collage to the group next time.

SESSION 11

Endings and Beginnings

This last session is about endings and beginnings. Over these past ten sessions, you have looked at abuse and trauma in women's lives; you have talked about how common it is in women's lives; you have examined how it has impacted you and others in the group; and you have learned some skills to move you further on your path toward healing.

Each person brought something special to this last session, and you each placed it in the center and created an "altar." An altar is a place where you can put things that are special to you in your life. These things represent or symbolize what is important to you—an event, a milestone, an accomplishment, a person, a loved pet, nature, something sacred—anything that is meaningful and personal. Creating an altar as we did in the group can be a way of honoring yourself.

▶ Here is a place where you can write or draw about the item you brought to group, why you chose to place it on the altar, and what you shared about its meaning to you with the other women in the group.

EXERCISE

APPRECIATION

1. What did you appreciate about the individual group members?

____

____

____

2. What did you appreciate about the group?

____

____

____

Ending a Relationship

Here are some guidelines you discussed in your group that are helpful when ending a relationship. Some of these helped us to end our group.

- Be direct and honest.
- Speak with "I" statements rather than "you" statements.
- Express feelings being experienced in the present.
- Assume personal responsibility for change.
- Decide the level of physical and emotional intimacy you want with the person.
- Act in a timely fashion—establish and adhere to agreed-upon timelines by which changes should occur.
- Let the other person know what you appreciate about her or him.
- Let the other person know what you appreciated about the relationship.
- Tell her or him what you wish you'd been able to do differently.

Spirituality

There are many ways to heal from trauma. Spirituality is a way to heal by gaining serenity and a sense of connection. Often, there is confusion about the terms *spirituality* and *religion*.

▶ What does *religion* mean to you?

_____

_____

▶ What does *spirituality* mean to you?

_____

_____

One definition of *spirituality* is "oneness, wholeness, connection to the universe; belief in something greater than yourself; trust in a higher or deeper part of yourself."

Connection is a word very commonly associated with *spirituality*. Spirituality often means connection on multiple levels:

- connection with self
- connection with others
- connection with nature, the earth
- connection to a Higher Power

༄

"I had an opportunity to share my feelings with myself

and with others—and to get all those ugly feelings out. I don't

feel as heavy-hearted as I did. Now I feel a lot of joy in my heart.

I walk with my head held high and my soul set free."

The Garden

The metaphor of a garden, reflected in the following quote, is helpful to many women because it describes the diversity of women's experience and expression of their spirituality.

> Gardens can be entered in a thousand ways and at any time. You can enter in childhood by the door of your home and continue to cultivate your garden through the whole of your life. Or the door can slam shut in adolescence, leaving you lost and searching for what T. S. Eliot called "the unknown, remembered gate." You can enter through a gate that is wide or narrow or so overgrown with ivy and weeds that you have to search carefully for the opening. . . . But who could argue that a garden of daisies and hollyhocks was more developed than a garden of artichokes and asparagus? Who could claim that a garden with a great variety of flowers was more inclusive and therefore more highly evolved than one that contained only roses? All gardens, of course, must be cultivated if they are to grow, but each one comes to maturity in its own time, in its own way. (Anderson and Hopkins 1993, 15)

Spiritual Practice

One of the ways that people develop their spirituality is through practice. With practice comes a deeper spiritual connection and healing. Women in Twelve Step programs practice Steps that are based on spiritual principles.

These mutual-help groups are free and readily available in most communities. There are groups for women who have experienced abuse, as well as groups for addiction recovery. This can be a place to find support from other women.

Think about how you can practice or get more in touch with your spiritual side.

Here are some examples:

- quiet time
- meditation
- prayer
- attending church, synagogue, mosque, temple
- centering activities such as singing or listening to music

- attending Twelve Step meetings

- being out in nature

- keeping a journal

- helping others in need

- creating personal altars

    This might be a grouping of personal items that are meaningful to you, such as a seashell from a memorable walk on the beach after a month of sobriety, a collar from a beloved pet, a photo of a significant person or event, a pinecone from a hike, a family photo, a prize from a fair, a candle. It can be a special location where you can stop, pause, reflect, pray, meditate, and feel connected to a sense of time and place, history, accomplishment, and hope.

- learning from others

    Holding a quiet, safe, respectful time where you, as women, can come together to share your hopes, dreams, and what is meaningful can be empowering. Sharing intimate stories can be inspiring and freeing.

- celebrations!

    Integrate celebrations, rituals, and traditions into your daily routine. As women, we need to learn to celebrate ourselves, even when we are alone. One example is celebrating milestones: birthdays, receiving a high school diploma or GED, staying clean and sober, sticking with an exercise program, and facing a tough problem. It is important to celebrate internal and external accomplishments. These celebrations can offer stability, direction, connection to your cultural roots, and reinforcement of positive conceptions of womanhood. Spiritual activities and rituals offer relationship and connection (with family, community, and peers), beliefs and values, healing, protection, support (others committed to helping you reach your goals), and celebration (joy and hope).

▶ How much time do you give yourself each week to allow for personal reflection, cultural traditions, or discussions about life, meaning, and values?

_____

_____

▶ If you want to change the role of spirituality in your life, how can you make that happen?

_____

_____

EXERCISE

MEDITATION

Meditation is one form of spiritual practice.

Meditation can help us find serenity in our world through solitude and stillness. It can help us feel calm and at peace deep inside. You can do meditation with your eyes open or closed.

> Breathing is central to meditation. Place both of your feet on the floor, empty your hands and laps, sit up straight, and close your eyes. If you prefer to keep your eyes open, place a special item in front of you (such as a candle, flower, or photo) and focus on it.

> *(You may want to have a friend read the following to you.)*

> Now, focus on the breath at the very end of your nose. Slowly and silently count to four as you inhale. Then count to four as you exhale. Keep breathing and counting. Follow your breath—the air—as it flows in and out of your nose.

> If other thoughts come to mind, just let them pass on through. Come back and focus on your breath. Count silently to four as you inhale. Count to four as you exhale.

> Continue this for one to two minutes. Then stop counting and just breathe.

> If feelings come up, recognize them but then let them pass. Let them go. Just keep bringing your attention back to your breathing, deep breaths going slowly in and slowly out again.

If you find your mind wandering, that is normal; do not be upset with
yourself. Just bring your mind gently back and concentrate on your breathing.

Keep focusing on your breath for a minute or two.

Please bring your attention back to the room. Feel your feet on the ground;
feel your back in your chair. When you are ready, open your eyes.

How does this feel for you?

You can create a silent space for yourself by taking a few minutes to do this every day,
maybe several times a day. If you are in a correctional setting, this is a particularly useful
tool to learn and practice. Meditation can help calm and soothe us. Remember, meditation is a way to create connection with our Higher Power and ourselves. This is another
skill we can use on our healing journey.

Meaningful Women in Our Lives

The amazing thing about connection is that it never really ends. When you
have a deep connection with another, it stays with you. Even if you do not
have contact with the person, you often still carry her or him with you.

In your group, you did an exercise about meaningful women. You thought
about the women who have been important to you—who have been meaningful
in your life. Maybe it was your mother, your grandmother, another family
member, a teacher, a therapist, or someone else. There may have been one
woman, or there may have been several.

EXERCISE

MEDITATION

▶ On the next page, write or draw about a woman (or women) who has touched your
life and made a difference. What did you receive from her? What did you learn or
what qualities did you respect?

What you each have been given is always there for you. . . . These enduring connections and their gifts are always there for you to receive. You just have to reach out and remember.

Our group has come to an end, but you can always carry this experience with you as you make new beginnings and decisions about the next steps in your life.

With each ending, space is created for new beginnings. I wish you all a great new beginning on your healing journey!

RESOURCES

Adult Children of Alcoholics World Service Organization, Inc.

ACA WSO
PO Box 3216
Torrance, CA 90510
(310) 534-1815
www.adultchildren.org

Alcoholics Anonymous

Grand Central Station
PO Box 459
New York, NY 10163
(212) 870-3400
www.aa.org

Co-Dependents Anonymous (CoDA)

Fellowship Services Office (FSO)
PO Box 33577
Phoenix, AZ 85067-3577
(602) 277-7991
www.codependents.org

Emotions Anonymous International

PO Box 4245
St. Paul, MN 55104-0245
(651) 647-9712
www.emotionsanonymous.org

Narcotics Anonymous

NAWS, Inc.
PO Box 9999
Van Nuys, CA 91409
(818) 773-9999
www.na.org

National Domestic Violence Hot Line

PO Box 161810
Austin, TX 78716
(800) 799-SAFE (7233) or
(800)-787-3224 (TTY)
www.ndvh.org

National Mental Health Consumers' Self-Help Clearinghouse

1211 Chestnut Street, Suite 1207
Philadelphia, PA 19107
(800) 553-4539
www.mhselfhelp.org

Parents Anonymous

675 West Foothill Blvd., Suite 220
Claremont, CA 91711-3475
(909) 621-6184
www.parentsanonymous.org

Posttraumatic Stress Disorder Alliance

PTSD Alliance Resource Center
(877) 507-PTSD (7873)
www.ptsdalliance.org

Survivors of Incest Anonymous World Service Office, Inc.

PO Box 190
Benson, MD 21018-9998
(410) 893-3322
www.siawso.org

Local Resources for Women in Abusive Relationships

Complete this resource list for your own area.

NAME OF PROGRAM	TYPE OF SERVICE	PHONE NUMBER

Local Resources for Women Who Have Experienced Abuse

Complete this resource list for your own area.

NAME OF PROGRAM	TYPE OF SERVICE	PHONE NUMBER

REFERENCES

American Psychiatric Association. 2000. *Diagnostic and statistical manual of mental disorders DSM-IV-TR (text revision).* 4th ed. Washington, D.C.: American Psychiatric Association.

Anderson, S., and P. Hopkins. 1993. *The feminine face of God: The unfolding of the sacred in women.* New York: Bantam.

Bloom, B., B. Owen, and S. Covington. 2003. *Gender responsive strategies: Research, practice, and guiding principles for women offenders.* Washington, D.C.: National Institute of Corrections.

Bureau of Justice Statistics. 1998. *National crime victimization survey.* Washington, D.C.: U.S. Department of Justice.

Carlson, B. 1990. Adolescent observers of marital violence. *Journal of Family Violence* 5:285–99.

Clarke, J., and C. Dawson. 1998. *Growing up again: Parenting ourselves, parenting our children.* Center City, Minn.: Hazelden.

Covington, S. 1999. *Helping women recover: A program for treating addiction (with a special edition for the CJ system).* San Francisco: Jossey-Bass.

———. 2000. *Awakening your sexuality: A guide for recovering women.* Center City, Minn.: Hazelden.

Covington, S., and L. Beckett. 1988. *Leaving the enchanted forest: The path from relationship addiction to intimacy.* San Francisco: HarperCollins Publishers.

Covington, S., and A. Dosher. 2000. The discipline of compassion. Unpublished manuscript.

Covington, S., and J. Surrey. 1997. The relational model of women's psychological development: Implications for substance abuse. In *Gender and alcohol: Individual and social perspectives,* edited by S. Wilsnack and R. Wilsnack, 335–51. New Brunswick, N.J.: Rutgers University Press.

Duluth Abuse Intervention Project. 1999. *Power and control wheel.* Duluth, Minn.: Minnesota Program Development.

Hopper, J. 1998. *Child abuse: Statistics, research, resources.* Boston: Boston University School of Medicine.

Miller, J. 1986. *What do we mean by relationships?* Work in Progress Working Paper Series, no. 22. Wellesley, Mass.: Stone Center, Wellesley College.

———. 1990. *Connections, disconnections, and violations.* Work in Progress Working Paper Series, no. 33. Wellesley, Mass.: Stone Center, Wellesley College.

Pollock, J. 2002. *Women, prison and crime.* Pacific Grove, Calif.: Brooks/Cole.

Ringel, C. 1997. *Criminal victimization in 1996, changes 1995–1996 with trends 1993–1996.* Washington, D.C.: U.S. Department of Justice, Bureau of Justice Statistics.

Duplicating this page is illegal. Do not copy this material without written permission from the publisher.

87

ABOUT THE AUTHORS

Stephanie S. Covington, Ph.D., LCSW

Stephanie S. Covington is a clinician, lecturer, and organizational consultant. She has over twenty-four years of experience in the design and implementation of treatment services for women and is recognized for her pioneering work in both the public and private sectors. Her consulting work ranges from the development of women's treatment programs at the Betty Ford Center and at Hanley-Hazelden in West Palm Beach to the creation of gender-responsive treatment for the Pennsylvania Department of Corrections. Educated at Columbia University and the Union Institute, she has conducted seminars for health professionals, business and community organizations, and recovery groups in the United States, Mexico, Europe, Africa, and New Zealand. Dr. Covington is based in La Jolla, California, where she is co-director of both the Institute for Relational Development and the Center for Gender and Justice.

Kary Young

Kary Young graduated with honors from Carleton University in Ottawa, Canada, where she majored in Women's Studies and Sociology. She has worked with Canadian national organizations on the issues of women's rights, reproductive rights, and citizens' advocacy. She is currently a research associate at the Center for Gender and Justice in La Jolla, California.

OTHER BOOKS BY STEPHANIE S. COVINGTON

Leaving the Enchanted Forest:
The Path from Relationship Addiction to Intimacy

A Woman's Way through the 12-Steps

A Woman's Way through the 12-Steps Workbook

Awakening Your Sexuality: A Guide for Recovering Women

Helping Women Recover: A Program for Treating Addiction
(with a special edition for use in the criminal justice system)

FEEDBACK FORM

Dear Recovering Woman:

I would appreciate hearing about your experience with the *Beyond Trauma* program. Any information you would like to share with me will be greatly appreciated.

Describe yourself.

_____

_____

_____

Describe where you participated in this program.

_____

_____

Describe your experience with the *Beyond Trauma* program.

_____

_____

_____

_____

_____

_____

_____

_____

What did you find most useful?

_____

_____

_____

_____

_____

What did you find least useful?

_____

_____

Why? How?

_____

_____

Other suggestions/comments:

_____

_____

_____

_____

Thank you for your input.

Stephanie S. Covington   FAX: (858) 454-8598
Center for Gender & Justice   E-mail: SSCIRD@aol.com
Institute for Relational Development
7946 Ivanhoe Avenue, Suite 201B
La Jolla, CA 92037